Message to Parents

Congratulations on your child's participation in the American Red Cross Swimming and Water Safety program. This booklet is an important part of your child's swimming experience. We encourage you and your child to read this booklet together during this session. It includes—

- A story line that supports and reinforces what your child is learning.
- Achievement cards that indicate your child's progress toward passing Red Cross Preschool Aquatics Levels 1 and 2 or Learn-to-Swim Level 1. Your child's instructor will complete the appropriate achievement card at the end of each session.
- Activities to help you practice with your child.
- General water safety tips to help you keep your family safe whenever you are in, on or around water.
- A chart that provides an overview of Red Cross Preschool Aquatics and Learn-to-Swim courses.

You can play a role in helping your child learn to swim by—

- Providing for your child's safety around water at all times.
- Maintaining enthusiasm and a positive attitude about learning to swim.
- Discussing and applying water safety rules.
- Ensuring that your child attends each swim lesson.
- Practicing the fundamental skills your child is learning in class.

Use the story to continue the discussion about your child's swim lesson experience. The achievement cards summarize the skills taught and serve as a guide for you to use to practice specific skills with your child.

Page 14 provides activities you can do with your child that reinforce the knowledge and skills learned during lessons. In the beginning, your child will likely require physical holding and support from you or flotation equipment, such as kickboards. As your child gains confidence and improves in ability, you can reduce and finally eliminate the physical support. You should always remain in the water and within arm's reach as you practice with your child at these levels. Keep it safe, but also have fun!

It cannot be overemphasized that participation in any swim lesson program will not "drownproof" your child. It is only the first step in developing your child's water safety and swimming skills. Year-round practice, regular exposure to water and positive encouragement are the tools needed for developing your child's comfort level in water and improving his or her swimming skills.

The Red Cross strongly recommends that a swimmer engage in water activities only where there is active adult supervision. Continue your child's swimming and water safety education by enrolling him or her in all the levels of Red Cross Preschool Aquatics and Learn-to-Swim.

Contact your local Red Cross chapter for further information.

Raffy Learns to Swim

This book belongs to _____

"Raffy! Raffy! Where are you? Time to go to your first swim lesson!" called Waddles excitedly. He stepped into her room to check on his little sister, Raffy, but she wasn't there! Just as he was about to leave, he heard something move. He looked over the bed and saw Raffy hiding underneath a beach towel. "What are you doing?" Waddles asked.

"I…I'm not going to my swim lesson," said Raffy, peeking from underneath the towel. "I don't want to learn how to swim."

"But Raffy, learning to swim is fun!" said Waddles. "Your teacher, Miss LaPink, will tell you about water safety and teach you how to be a good swimmer."

Feeling better, Raffy gathered up her towel, swimsuit, sunglasses and sunscreen. She followed Waddles downstairs and off to her first swim lesson.

3

At the pool, Waddles showed Raffy to her class, and then went to join his classmates. "Hi boys and girls. My name is Miss LaPink. I can see you are all ready to learn about water safety and to have some fun in the water," she said.

Everyone cheered, including Raffy.

9ft

5ft

3ft

4

"Be Cool, Follow the Rule!" Miss LaPink told the class. "That's the first rule. Following the rules will keep you safe."

"Another rule is: Swim with a Buddy in a Supervised Area. Does anyone know what that means?" Miss LaPink asked.

"Always swim with a friend and only when lifeguards or grown-ups are watching," said Zora Zebra eagerly.

"That's right," said Miss LaPink, "and always obey lifeguards. They help you stay safe and can help if you get hurt," she told the class.

1. Be Cool, Follow the Rule
2. Swim with a Buddy in a Supervised Area
3. Look Before You Leap
4. Don't Just Pack It, Wear Your Jacket
5. Think So You Don't Sink

Miss LaPink led the class to the shallow end of the pool. "Does anyone know how to tell the shallow end from the deep end of the pool?"

Raffy knew the answer to this one. "I can stand up in shallow water and keep my face dry and the deep water is where I can't touch the bottom," she said.

"That's right," said Miss LaPink. Miss LaPink pointed to the numbers on the pool wall. "These numbers tell you how deep the water is," she explained. "Always check to make sure the water isn't too shallow or too deep. The rule is: 'Look Before You Leap.' You wouldn't want to jump on somebody or something that could hurt you."

6

"Okay, let's get in the water and start learning to swim," Miss LaPink said to the class. "Steps, ladders, ramps or the sides of the pool are great ways to safely get in or out of the water."

One by one, the youngsters entered the water.

"Great job everyone! Let's all get in a circle," Miss LaPink told the class. "Can anyone put their face in the water?" she asked.

"I can! I can!" shouted Plato Platypus. Plato dipped his face into the water and then out again, smiling and wet.

"Very good, Plato! When I count to 3, everybody try it." Miss LaPink counted, "1...2...3."

On 3, everyone put their faces in the water.

"Wow!" exclaimed Miss LaPink. "That was great. Now you are ready to blow bubbles. Everyone needs a buddy to be sure you are blowing lots of bubbles."

Miss LaPink made Denver Dog and Raffy buddies. "You first, Raffy," Denver said, "I'll hold your hands."

Raffy wasn't sure about putting her face in the water and blowing bubbles. Her tail feathers were shaking. "Ready! Go!"

Slowly, Raffy took a deep breath and put her face in the water.

Denver counted, "1...2...3," while Raffy blew bubbles. When she finished, she shook the water from her feathers and laughed, "This is fun!"

Raffy and her classmates learned how to float on their fronts and backs. They learned how to roll over from their fronts to their backs. Raffy even learned how to stay in one place without touching the bottom. "This is called treading water," Miss LaPink explained.

Raffy loved her swim lessons. She practiced at home just as Miss LaPink said. She was eager to show her mom and dad how much she learned every day.

9

Finally the class was ready to start stroking with their arms and kicking their legs. Miss LaPink made sure everyone in the class got lots of practice. They were all getting so good!

Raffy could not believe all the great things she was able to do in the water. "I'm so glad I'm learning to swim!" exclaimed Raffy.

Preschool Aquatics
Level 1
Achievement Card

Instructor:_____

Date:_____

Skills

❑ Enter water using ladder, steps or side

❑ Exit water using ladder, steps or side

❑ Blowing bubbles through mouth and nose, 3 seconds

❑ Submerging mouth, nose and eyes

❑ Opening eyes under water and retrieving submerged objects, 2 times (in shallow water)

❑ Front glide, 2 body lengths

❑ Recover from a front glide to a vertical position

❑ Back glide, 2 body lengths

❑ Back float, 3 seconds

❑ Recover from a back float to a vertical position

❑ Roll from front to back

❑ Roll from back to front

❑ Treading with arm and hand actions (in chest-deep water)

❑ Alternating leg action on front, 2 body lengths

❑ Simultaneous leg action on front, 2 body lengths

❑ Alternating arm action on front, 2 body lengths

❑ Simultaneous arm action on front, 2 body lengths

❑ Combined arm and leg actions on front, 2 body lengths

❑ Alternating leg action on back, 2 body lengths

❑ Simultaneous leg action on back, 2 body lengths

❑ Alternating arm action on back, 2 body lengths

❑ Simultaneous arm action on back, 2 body lengths

❑ Combined arm and leg actions on back, 2 body lengths

Safety Topics

❑ Staying safe around aquatic environments

❑ Recognizing the lifeguards

❑ Don't just pack it, wear your jacket

❑ Recognizing an emergency

❑ How to call for help

❑ Too much sun is no fun

Exit Skills Assessment

❑ Enter independently, using either the ladder, steps or side, travel at least 5 yards, submerge to mouth and blow bubbles for at least 3 seconds then safely exit the water. (Children can walk, move along the gutter or "swim.")

❑ While in shallow water, glide on front at least 2 body lengths, then roll to back and float on back for 3 seconds then recover to a vertical position.

Note: All skills are demonstrated with support in this level.

▢ **I Passed!**

Preschool Aquatics
Level 2
Achievement Card

Instructor:_____

Skills

❑ Enter water by stepping in

❑ Exit water using ladder, steps or side

❑ Bobbing, 3 times

❑ Opening eyes under water and retrieving submerged objects, 2 times (in chest-deep water)

❑ Front float, 3 seconds

❑ Front glide, 2 body lengths

❑ Recover from a front float or glide to a vertical position (in chest-deep water)

❑ Back float, 5 seconds

❑ Back glide, 2 body lengths

❑ Recover from a back float or glide to a vertical position (in chest-deep water)

❑ Roll from front to back

❑ Roll from back to front

❑ Treading using arm and leg actions, 5 seconds (in shoulder-deep water)

❑ Combined arm and leg actions on front, 3 body lengths

❑ Finning arm action on back, 3 body lengths

❑ Combined arm and leg actions on back, 3 body lengths

Learn-to-Swim Level 1

Achievement Card

Date:_____

Instructor:_____

Date:_____

Safety Topics

- Staying safe around aquatic environments
- Recognizing the lifeguards
- Don't just pack it, wear your jacket
- Recognizing an emergency
- How to call for help
- Too much sun is no fun

Exit Skills Assessment

- Glide on front at least 2 body lengths, roll to back, float on back for 5 seconds then recover to a vertical position.
- Glide on back for at least 2 body lengths, roll to front, float for 5 seconds then recover to a vertical position.
- Swim using combined arm and leg actions on front for 3 body lengths, roll to back, float for 5 seconds, roll to front then continue swimming on front for 3 body lengths.

Note: All skills are demonstrated with assistance in this level.

▢ I Passed!

Skills

- ❏ Enter water using ladder, steps or side
- ❏ Exit water using ladder, steps or side
- ❏ Blowing bubbles through mouth and nose, 3 seconds
- ❏ Bobbing, 3 times
- ❏ Opening eyes under water and retrieving submerged objects, 2 times (in shallow water)
- ❏ Front glide, 2 body lengths
- ❏ Recover from a front glide to a vertical position
- ❏ Back glide, 2 body lengths
- ❏ Back float, 3 seconds
- ❏ Recover from a back float or glide to a vertical position
- ❏ Roll from front to back
- ❏ Roll from back to front
- ❏ Treading using arm and hand actions (in chest-deep water)
- ❏ Alternating leg action on front, 2 body lengths
- ❏ Simultaneous leg action on front, 2 body lengths
- ❏ Alternating arm action on front, 2 body lengths
- ❏ Simultaneous arm action on front, 2 body lenghts
- ❏ Combined arm and leg actions on front, 2 body lengths
- ❏ Alternating leg action on back, 2 body lengths

- ❏ Simultaneous leg action on back, 2 body lengths
- ❏ Alternating arm action on back, 2 body lengths
- ❏ Simultaneous arm action on back, 2 body lengths
- ❏ Combined arm and leg actions on back, 2 body lengths

Safety Topics

- ❏ Staying safe around aquatic environments
- ❏ Recognizing the lifeguards
- ❏ Don't just pack it, wear your jacket
- ❏ Recognizing an emergency
- ❏ How to call for help
- ❏ Too much sun is no fun

Exit Skills Assessment

- ❏ Enter independently, using either the ladder, steps or side, travel at least 5 yards, bob 3 times then safely exit the water. (Participants can walk, move along the gutter or "swim.")
- ❏ Glide on front at least 2 body lengths, roll to a back float for 3 seconds and recover to a vertical position. (This part of the assessment can be performed with support.)

▢ I Passed!

Helping Your Child Progress

Safety Tour

Take your child on a guided tour of the swimming area. Show him or her the deep water and other spots that are dangerous. Explain the rules of the swimming area. Be sure your child knows that the swimming area is off limits unless an adult is present to supervise.

Breath Control

Blowing Bubbles—Encourage your child to blow bubbles at the surface of the water or while submerged by suggesting images that are familiar, such as—

- Blowing out a candle, away a dandelion or through a straw.
- Blowing an instrument, such as a trumpet, saxophone or bugle.
- Making a tugboat or jet engine-motor noise.

Submersion

Treasure Hunting—Place a variety of objects that sink on the bottom of the pool. Have your child retrieve the objects. If the water is too deep, hold the items under water. If necessary, assist your child gently with a press on the back to help him or her submerge. Be sure to let your child know that you are going to help!

Locomotion

Transformers—Have your child think of his or her favorite action character to portray. You can provide support by holding your child or by having him or her use a floating object, such as a large ball, kickboard or barbell, to propel to another part of the pool as that action figure. Suggest different ways for your child to propel him- or herself, such as jumping, using arm strokes and kicking.

Be an Animal—Have your child pretend to move like different kinds of animals. You can provide support by holding your child or by having him or her use a floating object, such as a large ball, kickboard or barbell, to move like that animal to another part of the pool. Use your imagination, but here are some suggestions to be sure that your child varies the movements:

- Hop like a bunny or a kangaroo
- Move like a snake on your side
- Move like an inchworm with your arms stretched out and your body moving up and down
- Stroke like a puppy
- Swim like a frog or a dolphin

14

All Skills

Simon Says—Explain that you are going to say and do skills, such as kicking, arm strokes and blowing bubbles. Explain that if you say the words, "Simon Says," he or she should do the skills that you say. Explain that if you do not say the words, "Simon Says," he or she should not move. Consider the following skills:

- Getting in the water in different ways (using the stairs, ladder or side)
- Getting out of the water in different ways (using the stairs, ladder or side)
- Blowing bubbles
- Arms stroking at the same time
- Arms stroking in an alternating motion
- Holding on to the wall and kicking with legs moving at the same time
- Holding on to the wall and kicking with legs moving in an alternating motion
- Walking forward and then changing direction of travel

Be Water Smart

General Water Safety Tips

Follow these general water safety tips whenever swimming in any body of water (pools, lakes, ponds, quarries, canals, rivers or oceans):

- Always swim with a buddy; never swim alone.
- Read and obey all rules and posted signs.
- Swim only in lifeguard-supervised areas.
- Children or inexperienced swimmers should take extra precautions, such as wearing U.S. Coast Guard-approved life jackets, when around the water.
- Watch out for the "dangerous too's"—too tired, too cold, too far from safety, too much sun and too much strenuous activity.
- Set water safety rules for your family based on swimming abilities (for example, inexperienced swimmers should stay in water less than chest deep).
- Be knowledgeable of the water environment you are in and its potential hazards, such as deep and shallow areas, currents, depth changes, obstructions and entry and exit points. The more informed you are, the more aware you will be of hazards and safe practices.
- Know how to prevent, recognize and respond to emergencies.
- Use a feetfirst entry when entering the water.
- Enter headfirst only when the area is clearly marked for diving and has no obstructions.

Watching Children Around Water

- Maintain constant supervision. Watch children around any water (such as pools, rivers, lakes, bath tubs, toilets and even buckets of water), no matter how well your child can swim and no matter how shallow the water. Stay attentive; do not drink alcohol while supervising.
- If there are small children in your home, use safety locks on toilets, keep toilet-bowl covers down and bathroom doors closed and empty bath tubs after use.
- Empty cleaning buckets immediately after use.
- Stay within an arm's reach of an inexperienced swimmer while he or she is in the water.
- Do not rely on substitutes. The use of flotation devices and inflatable toys cannot replace parental supervision. Such devices could suddenly shift position, lose air or slip out from underneath, leaving the child in a dangerous situation.
- Prevent access to water features, such as small ponds and waterfalls.
- Empty kiddie pools immediately after use. Do not leave water in an unattended pool of any kind.
- When visiting another home, check the site for potential water hazards and always supervise your children.
- Teach children to swim by enrolling them in Red Cross Preschool Aquatics and Learn-to-Swim courses. Your decision to provide your child with early aquatic experiences is a gift that will have lifelong rewards.
- Family members should participate in a Red Cross water safety course. Water safety courses encourage safe practices and provide lifelong safety skills.
- Learn first aid, cardiopulmonary resuscitation (CPR) and how to use an automated external defibrillator (AED). Parents and other caregivers, such as grandparents, older siblings and babysitters, should take a first aid and CPR/AED course. Knowing these skills can be important around the water, and will expand your capabilities in providing care for your child.
- Contact your local Red Cross for further information on enrolling in swimming, water safety, first aid and CPR/AED courses.